NOW YOU CAN PLAY

90s hits 1

IMP

International MUSIC Publications

International Music Publications Limited
Griffin House 161 Hammersmith Road London W6 8BS England

DON'T BE A MUSIC COPYCAT!

The copying of © copyright material is a criminal offence and may lead to prosecution.

Series Editor: Sadie Cook

Editorial & production: Artemis Music Limited
Design & production: Space DPS Limited

Published 1999

International MUSIC Publications

International Music Publications

England: Griffin House
161 Hammersmith Road
London W6 8BS

Germany: Marstallstr. 8
D-80539 München

Denmark: Danmusik
Vognmagergade 7
DK1120 Copenhagen K

Italy: Via Campania 12
20098 San Giuliano Milanese
Milano

Spain: Magallanes 25
28015 Madrid

France: 20 Rue de la Ville-l'Eveque
75008 Paris

Australia: 3 Talavera Road
North Ryde
New South Wales 2113

Scandinavia: P.O. Box 533
Vendevagen 85 B
S-182 15 Danderyd
Sweden

NOW YOU CAN PLAY 90s hits 1

Don't Let Go (Love)

Words and Music by Ivan Matias, Andrea Martin,
Marqueze Etheridge and Organized Noize

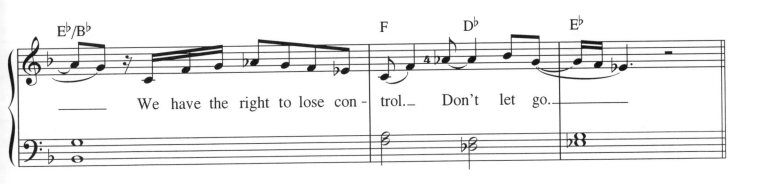

6

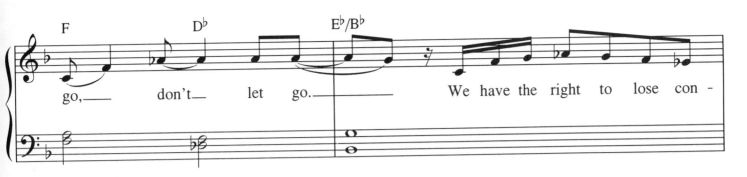

Verse 2
I often fantasize the stars above are watching
They know my heart, how I speak to you is like only lovers do
If I could wear your clothes, I'd pretend I was you
And lose control. Oh
There'll be some love making, heartbreaking, soul shaking love
Love making, heartbreaking, soul shaking

What's it gonna be? etc

Believe

Words and Music by Brian Higgins,
Stuart McLennan, Paul Barry,
Stephen Torch, Matt Gray and Tim Powell

Moderately

No mat - ter how___   hard I try___   you keep push - ing
Verse 2 see block lyric

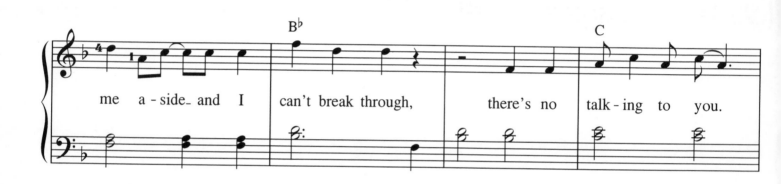

me a - side_ and I   can't break through,   there's no   talk - ing to you.

It's so   sad_____ that you're   leav - ing, takes   time_____ to be -

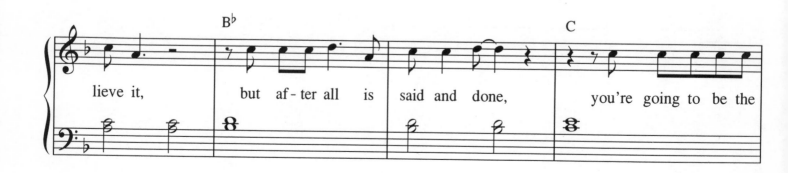

lieve it,   but af - ter all is   said and done,   you're going to be the

lone - ly one,_ oh._ Do you be - lieve_ in life_ af - ter love?

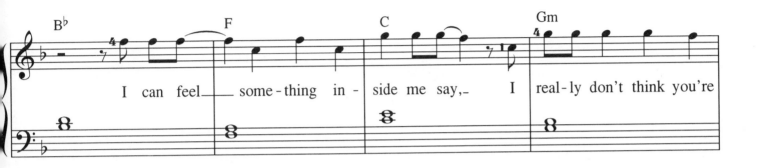

I can feel_ some - thing in - side me say,_ I real - ly don't think you're

strong e - nough, no._ Do you be - lieve_ in life_ af - ter love?

I can feel_ some - thing in - side me say,_ I real - ly don't think you're

strong e - nough, no._ But I know_ that I'll get through this,

strong e - nough, no.— Do you be - lieve__ in life_ af-ter love?

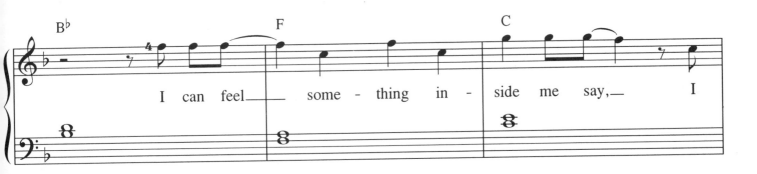

I can feel__ some - thing in - side me say,— I

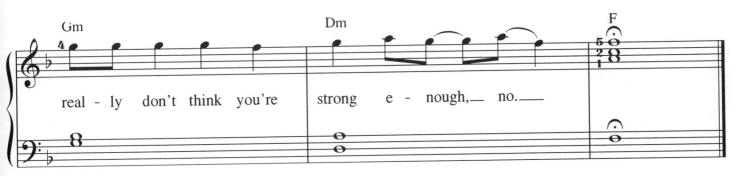

real - ly don't think you're strong e - nough,__ no.__

Verse 2
What am I supposed to do
Sit around and wait for you
And I can't do that
There's no turning back
I need time to move on
I need love to feel strong
'Cause I've had time to think it through
And maybe I'm too good for you, oh

Do you believe, etc

How Do I Live

Words and Music by
Diane Warren

Moderately slow

How do I_____ get through one night with - out___ you. If I had to
Verse 2 see block lyric

live with - out you, what kind of life would that be?___ Oh___

I,_____ I need you in my arms, need you to hold.___ You're my

world, my heart, my soul.___ If you ev - er leave,___

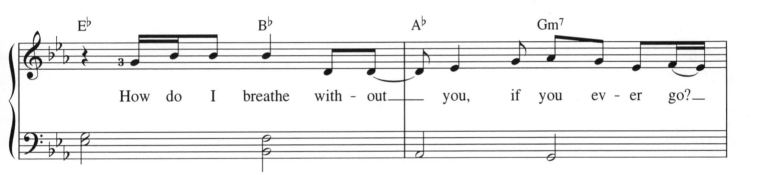

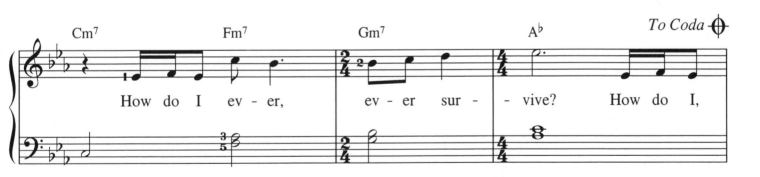

CODA

how do I, oh, how do I live

with - out you?

poco rall.

Verse 2
Without you, there'd be no sun in the sky
There would be no love in my life
There'd be no world left for me
And I , baby, I don't know what I would do
I'd be lost if I lost you
If you ever leave
Baby, you would take away everything real in my life

And tell me now etc

I Just Wanna Be Loved

Words and Music by George O'Dowd,
Jon Moss, Michael Craig and Roy Hay

Moderately

Take a pic - ture of to - night and keep it in your heart.
Verse 2 see block lyric

What is left is me - mo - ries,— there's no bet - ter way to part.—

I will find a - no - ther love, some - one who won't bring me down.

To Coda ⊕

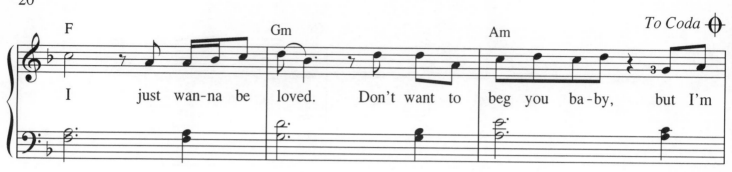

I just wan-na be loved. Don't want to beg you ba-by, but I'm

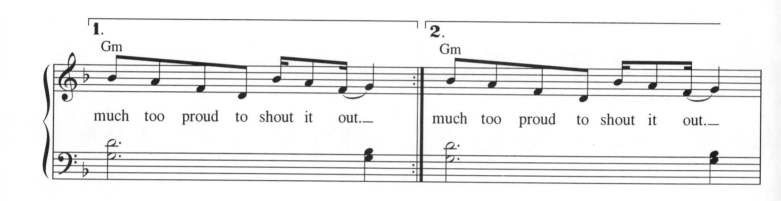

1. much too proud to shout it out.___ **2.** much too proud to shout it out.___

When you love some - one___ don't ya know,___ love is

blind.___ When you love some - one,___ they don't

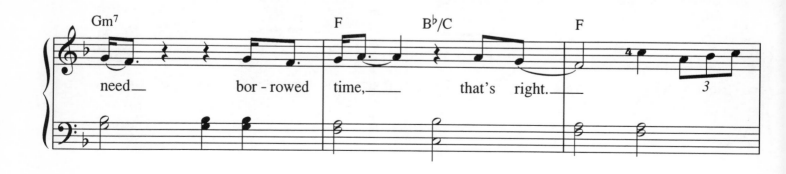

need___ bor - rowed time,___ that's right.___

D.S. al Coda

🜋 **CODA**

much too proud to shout it out.   I   just wan-na be   loved.—   Oh,—

I   just wan-na be   loved.—   Oh,—   I   just wan-na be

loved.—   Oh, I   just wan-na be   loved._

Verse 2
Take a piece of dignity and use it in your life
Even though you hurt me, I still want you to survive
Love was never special, we were never down
You will always have someone to bring you homeward bound

Fortunately I got wise this time, etc

I'll Be There For You

Words and Music by
Phil Solem, Marta Kauffman, David Crane,
Michael Skloff, Allee Willis and Danny Wilde

Bright rock

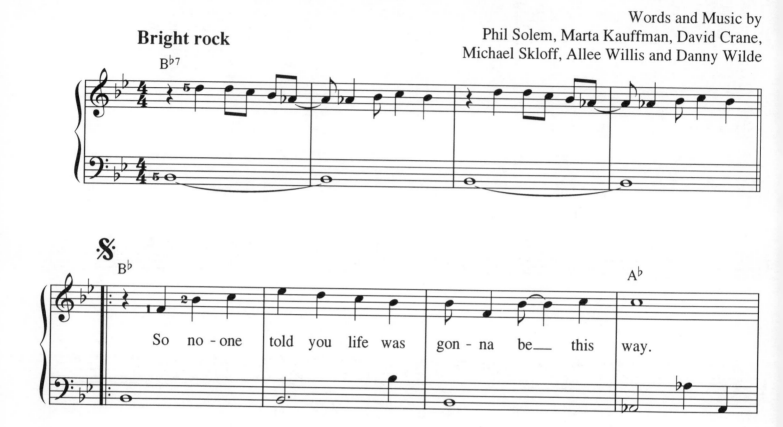

So no-one told you life was gon - na be— this way.

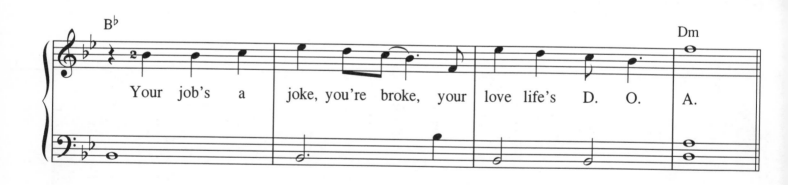

Your job's a joke, you're broke, your love life's D. O. A.

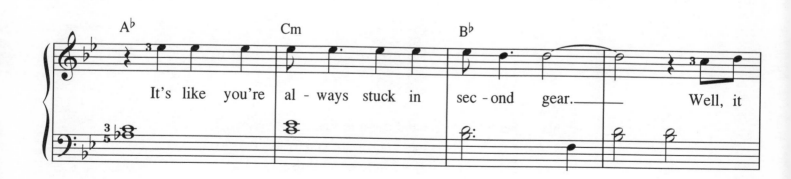

It's like you're al - ways stuck in sec - ond gear.___ Well, it

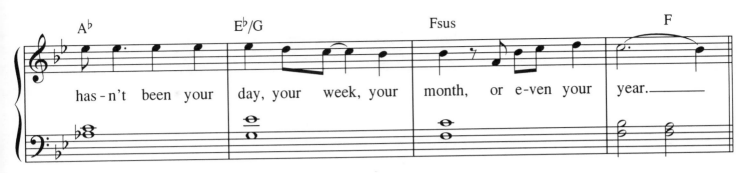

has-n't been your day, your week, your month, or e-ven your year.——

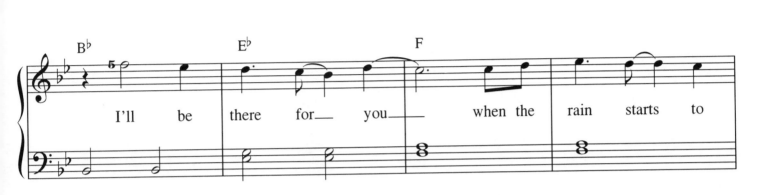

I'll be there for— you—— when the rain starts to

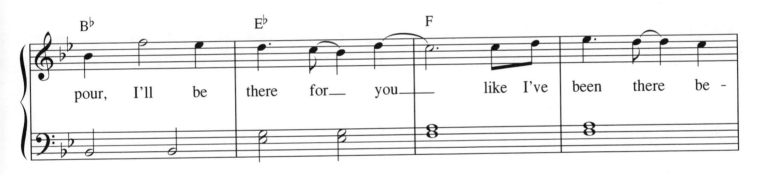

pour, I'll be there for— you—— like I've been there be-

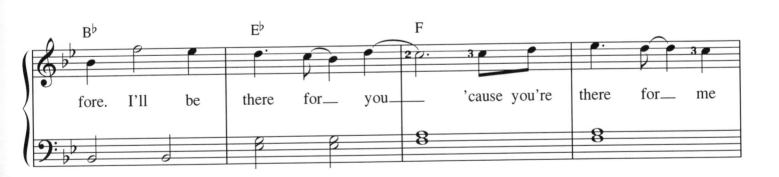

fore. I'll be there for— you—— 'cause you're there for— me

To Coda

1.

2.

too.

Lady Marmalade

Words and Music by
Bob Crewe and Kenny Nolan

Put Your Arms Around Me

Words and Music by
John McElhone, Sharleen Spiteri,
Robert Hodgens and Dave Stewart

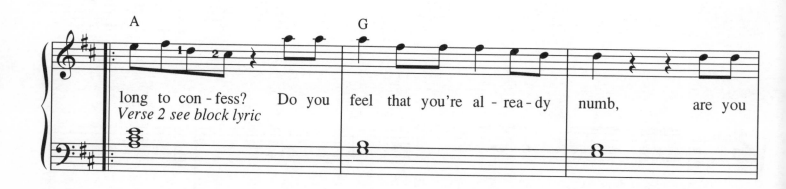

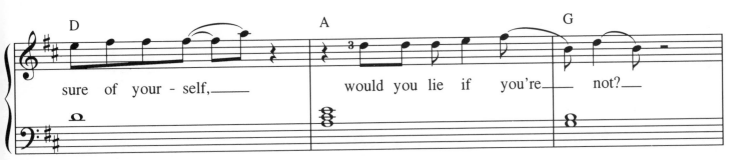

sure of your - self,_____ would you lie if you're___ not?___

You tire__ me out,___ don't want to let that hap - pen.

A se - cret scream so loud why did you let that hap - pen?

Ooh, ooh,___ so put your arms a - round me,__ you let me be - lieve that

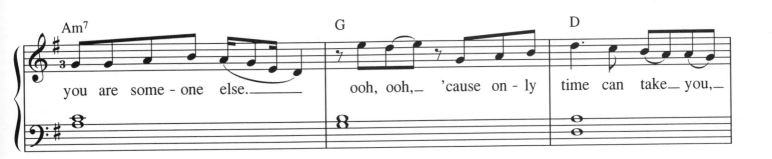

you are some - one else._____ ooh, ooh,__ 'cause on - ly time can take__ you,__

Take me, take me | some-where,— | some-where.— | Oh let me be - lieve.—

'cause on - ly | time can take you,—— | so | stop!

Verse 2
Maybe are you ready to break?
Do you think that I push you too far?
Would you open yourself
Are you reckless or not?
You tire me out, don't want to let that happen

A secret dream scream so loud, etc

Something About The
Way You Look Tonight

Words and Music by
Elton John and Bernie Taupin

There was a time___ I was ev-ery-thing and no-thing all in
Verse 2 see block lyric

one.___ When you found me___ I was

feel-ing like___ a cloud a-cross the sun.___ Oh I need to

tell___ you how you light up ev-ery sec-ond of the

look to-night.— The way you look to-night.— The way you look to-night.

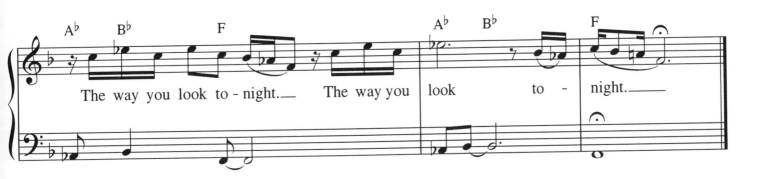

The way you look to-night.— The way you look to-night.——

Verse 2
With your smile
You pull the deepest secrets from my heart
In all honesty
I'm speechless and I don't know where to start

And I can't explain, etc

Together Again

Words and Music by Janet Jackson,
James Harris III, Terry Lewis and René Elizondo Jr

get my ba - - by. What I'd give just to

hold you close.__ As on earth,__ in hea - ven__ we will be to -

geth - er ba - by. To - geth - er a - gain my ba - by.

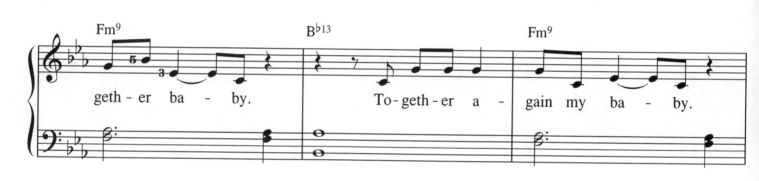

Ev - 'ry - where I go,__ ev - 'ry smile I see,__

__ I know you are there,__ smil - in' back at me.__ Danc - in' in moon - light,

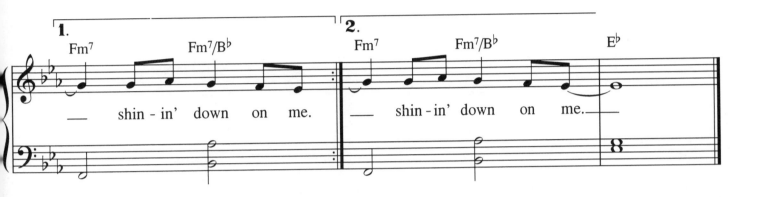

Verse 2

Always been a true angel to me

Now above, I can't wait for you to wrap your wings around me, baby

Wrap them around me baby

Sometimes I hear you whisperin' no more pain

No more worries will you ever see again

I'm so happy for my baby

Dream about us together again, etc

Where's The Love

Words and Music by Isaac Hanson,
Taylor Hanson, Zachary Hanson,
Mark Hudson and Steven Salover

Moderate rock

Some-thing's been go - ing on— and I don't— know what it is.—
Verse 2 see block lyric

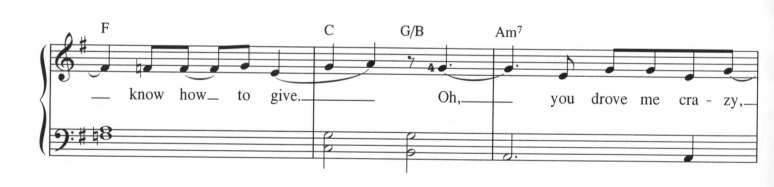

Woh.— You don't mind the tak - ing, girl,— but you don't—

— know how— to give.— Oh,— you drove me cra - zy,—

— but I don't know ba - by.— You're thin - king that it's me you're fool - ing.

2.

Eb / F / G / E

'round and 'round and 'round.___ Dark clouds all a - round,

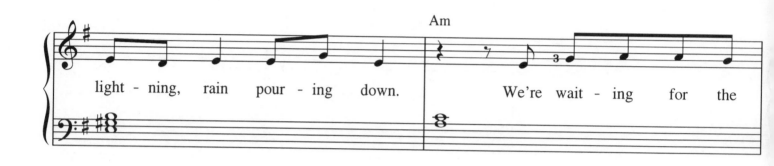

Am

light - ning, rain pour - ing down. We're wait - ing for the

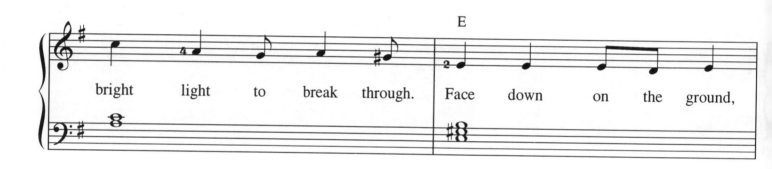

E

bright light to break through. Face down on the ground,

F

pick us up at the lost and found. We've got to change our point of view

G / A / Bm7

if we want the sky blue.___ Oh, we're seg - re - gat - ing,___

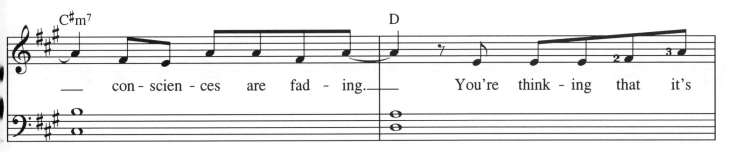

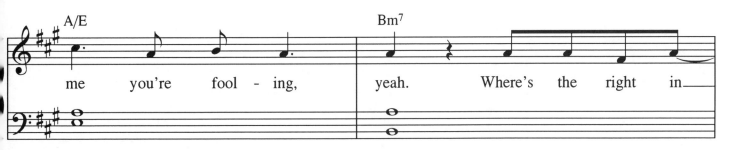

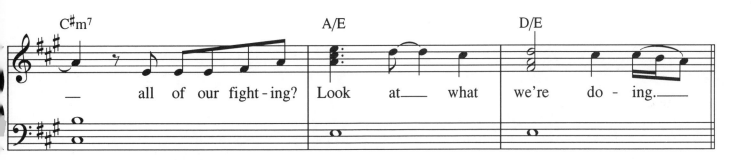

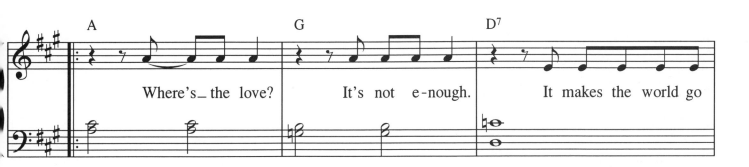

Verse 2

Can you tell me what you see whenever you look around?

We're tripping up all over ourselves and pulling each other down

Oh, we're separating, consciousness is fading

You're thinking that it's me you're fooling, etc

Printed in England
The Panda Group · Haverhill · Suffolk · 5/99